IN NO TIME

PRAISE FOR IN NO TIME

"In No Time folds the fabric of spacetime in masterful ways. Fasten your seatbelt for the journey of a lifetime!"
Ella Maclaren, Consultant, New York, USA

" … sensual, cerebral, as beguiling as it is different. This book isn't scant, it has prodigious breadth – I loved it!".
Alia K, London, UK

"I found In No Time deep, rich, touching and funny. The deceptively chatty style puts you on every-day terms with historical characters".
E Garcia, Brazil

"This writing has energy; she's the Action Painter of words".
G Freeman, Illinois USA

"A genre-defying delight; 'New Age' concepts meet scientific pragmatism".
Jay Rocha, London

ACKNOWLEDGEMENTS

My warmest thanks and gratitude to Nick Williams, author of the life changing best-seller *The Work We Were Born To Do* for his belief and pivotal support, and to David Caddy, poet and founding editor of the inspiring Literary Journal *Tears In The Fence* for his manuscript appraisal and unerring encouragement.

Huge thanks to my superlative family and friends around the globe for their love and support, and to readers for their time and considered comments,

To all of the above for being my soul tribe, I give thanks from the North-West corner of my heart

IN NO TIME

Eternal Realm of Eros the Life Force

JACQUELINE SULLIVAN

Ford Hill Press

Published by Ford Hill Press
www.fordhillpress.com

A CIP record for this book is available from the British Library

ISBN: 978-1-7397400-0-9

Printed in the UK by Amazon KDP Print

Front cover art: *Vermillion Zone* from the series *Tapestry,* by the author. Depicting two pairs of lips as one, the work was inspired by an Egyptian engraving symbolizing divine union.

To my daughter Anna

CONTENTS

Children of the Stars

Can we perchance side-step the laws that govern our coming into being, or must an endless cycle be our inexorable path from the warmth of the womb to the cold, cold tomb, we children of the stars?

Will, to paraphrase the poet in his quartet on time and the divine, our end be in our beginning?

In the beginning it is hot and dense, a sweltering morass of particles that instantly decay; their remnants destroy one another. Expansion and cooling create protons and neutrons; heat destroys the isotope produced. Further cooling allows it to form, creating elements that coalesce into galaxies and stars.

Time passes.

A voluptuous expansion and contraction of stars cause a fusion of elements that explode into the firmament as stardust, creating kumquats, gnats, shrimp-eating leafy sea creatures, people, and every material thing.

Galaxies collide destroying one another; new stars are born from the ruins.

PART ONE
FLUX

Loss of Face

(Tunnelling to the beginning of time:1)

I scroll down the comments.

Nosh-Nosh says *be thankful you still have your sight and working legs; what you need more than prayer is a lawyer.* Anonymous says *Don't expect pity from me; it was purely voluntary, dipshit.* Lionguy says *even though your face is a mess, never give up spirit till the LAST.*

I'd wanted to turn back time and now crave it. Engulfing myself in obscure scientific papers on temporal realms at the edge of known physics where the smallest unit of time is less than a trillionth of an attosecond and attoseconds drag like eons, I learn that, as Einstein tried to explain, time may not even exist.

This helps.

I replay events in chaotic order, watching myself in a world that seems strange and unreal. My 'father' refuses me the loan - doesn't home in on his inner pocket reminding me of Nelson or hand me a cheque saying May you're no beauty and you never will be or say you're okay as you are instead of booking my flight on Expedia.

But in 'reality' I *do* go ahead. Weeks later, deep dented

fissures spreading out like the sun appear on both cheeks as though my face is dissolving. I search the mirror but my sense of self, always precarious, is lost; I'm like the man from the banks of the Madre de Dios whose soul was stolen by an Instamatic.

****

Before that; before what happens happens.

Just days before I'm tangling with the giants, or discover their alliance is impassioned or that my secret kith and kin are embroiled in their ripping apart, there is leaving for Basel - gathering my bags, pondering the gilt-framed portrait that turns out to be me in our hallway mirror, then stepping jauntily out. It's warmish, around lunchtime. Tangles of leaves in our small walled oasis are moist with light drizzle. I'm about to fetch my umbrella when a patient, the umbrella-phobic Marvin, calls; you think that would prompt me, but no. I go through the gate, the thunder of London comes in - booming traffic barrelling up and down with the deafening roar of Niagara as I flag down a cab for Heathrow.

My unhinging hinges on forgetting my umbrella.

Basel...

... birthplace of Jung, dusk; the fairy-tale Munster glows like a lantern high on cathedral hill. My sixth sense is strong, I feel the spirit of my tribe. Even so next day when, somewhere near a dilapidated haberdashery outlet, I imagine I *hear* Jung expounding across the space-time continuum,

I'm unsettled. Worse; torn between allegiances and dodging the convention in favour of the *Antikenmuseum*, I'm immersed in tantalising tales of the maverick pharaoh and queen when a sense of fusion overwhelms me, forcing me to wonder: *could this be the slippery slope – feeling I'm somebody else while remaining aware of myself?*

Starbucks Claraplatz, remembering …
… joining Giles in an experiment on telepathy. Our EEG's recorded the same brain patterns, though only I had received the stimuli. Our report said 'a touching thought transference was evidenced in this passionate pair'.

Anticipation excites. I fumble in my bag and pull out a box: *Teuscher's signature Champagne Truffles.* I post them in my mouth as though feeding coins to a meter, painting my lips with molten Dom Perignon-soaked chocolate ganache, then soften them between my tongue and palate till they slither down my throat like oysters.

London next day.
I trip lightly past my stepfather's practice with barely a shudder but by the time I reach the salon, mirrors expose me endlessly looking uneasy in every reflection. Back outside I probe my new image in every shop window. Here's my head in the bakery, in the same dimension as a drum of baguettes; here it looms by a cash machine seen inside Barclays bank. I smile but I swear my phantom self doesn't. Puzzled, and lashed by monsoon-like rain I run home for dry clothes

instead of going straight to meet Giles as arranged.

Early evening; our home.

In the gilt-framed mirror my made-over face is a melting clown's, my hair a wet rat's coat. Squelching upstairs and across the landing my sodden shoes make blobs on the carpet like pieces of bread for retracing my route and I hear before I catch sight, which poses the question: _to see or not to see?_ I open the door.

Our bedroom …

… lit by the Egyptian pierced-brass lamp. Reflections from its stained-glass insets throw rainbows across Giles's back as Alison his colleague, spotting me from somewhere beneath him, utters profanities. I turn away but the scene is repeated in our tilted carved Cheval mirror. I'm a thing on a wire, controlled by an invisible stagehand, an unwilling nymph swooping in from stage left looking down on the Bacchanal. It's not Andromeda slamming into us but it turns _my_ world; hurls me from hearth and home into hitherto hidden, forbidden realms.

My road to ruin is as torrid as the Big Bang itself, my coming back into being as weird as the Llanwrtyd bog snorkelling trials.

PART TWO
IMPLOSION

Memories, Dreams,

Divine Compensation

Half conscious, soot dark; the bed weighing down near my feet, the grip of terror at my throat, a man's voice booming, chastising me. My arm swings out, feeling for the switch on the bedside lamp. '*Leave it!*' he orders. I feel the weight lift; hear the springs of the mattress go ping as the man moves to widen the chink in the door.

'*More conducive*', he whispers. Amber light blossoms and insinuates itself.

He begins the session. In the gloom I furtively venerate his stature, his penetrating eyes. He tells me to face away so I won't be inhibited from sharing my thoughts - my thoughts have become disturbing, seeming to arise independently of me, from some alien, external source.

'Normal for your dissociative state', Jung tells me.

I'm on the brink of a genuine insight when he interjects, griping about Freud. I ask what he thinks about Nietzsche. 'Nietzsche', he says; 'those who knew him personally ridiculed his manner of playing the piano', then switches subject abruptly again. 'The important thing', he tells me as I shift around, staying in his shadow to hide my imperfections, 'is that you have iron in your soul; you *can* seek your own transformation!' This emboldens me to question his piece on Picasso's Blue Period - I'm a bit of a coward so I'm jittery, but I've fleetingly glimpsed my Warrior self, so I confide I find his personality electric, his charisma erotically unsettlingly.

He artfully replies that people in Antiquity embraced sexuality in their spirituality, making them less prone to psychic disturbance.

By now I'm regretting my Debenham's winter pyjamas.

As he makes to leave - as suddenly as he appeared - I feel calmed, and in the same breath moved by this sturdy, vivacious, exuberant man who now delivers his parting shot: Time to recover the Chthonic spirit, he says. Earthy; the dark side; the *alter*!

Funny he should say that....

Alter

Divine Eros

Continue plagued by interference, voices off; like an interrupted radio signal there's frequent oscillation in range in my waking consciousness. Here I am, beauty of the desert, performing erotic gyrations designed to elicit arousal, my principal duty as the feminine aspect of deity incarnate. Here in the Lightlands the state of desire and physical love are routes to the realm where humanity meets divinity.

As heavily scented smoke spirals heavenwards I soar to formless, dimensionless realms.

In lucid moments I attribute these episodes to the echo of the Collective Unconscious, or the First Law of Thermodynamics, ie: universal energy is constant, can't be destroyed and can only change forms. As a psychotherapist I keep my own counsel; I may not always be May by day. Or night.

Nefertiti my sweet, says Pharaoh, tugging at the tie beneath his jawline. Adjusting his false beard he slingshots a box down the table towards me. Eagle-eying Pharaoh I take out the bling. Akhenaten, sensual, mystical king some call Beast to my Beauty looks through no fault of his own, with his long fleshy earlobes, full fleshy lips and distended gut, like a cross between an elongated Buddha and a pot-bellied pig. But the sex is good and the jewellery's not bad.

Lightlands

While virtual passion isn't *bad,* it just doesn't cut it. My colourless world of having to start over all over begins with a relic of student days.

Black iron railings frame a grey world wrapped around a hard, grey quadrangle. Grey cement steps decked with multi-hued fluids; a rat dashing by as I beat a path to his door in a wall as grim as a Cat A landing. The smell greets me before he does, the stench of blocked drains and stale ashtrays.

A spliff or three; a bottle of Sainsbury's Shiraz from mugs with no handles. On the bamboo couch with a rickety frame that digs in, on the tattered, rancid-smelling carpet he dredges the depths of me, discovering my need as deep as his half-crazed craving. We haven't used anything and I haven't protested, even though I've brought something with me. I think suddenly of my laptop, mentally inserting the drive I'd used in internet cafés. Panic rises like bile; *removable drives plugged in and pulled out promiscuously. What if my CPU is infected? What if it's beyond repair?*

Suddenly he drops a white pill with a heart-shaped logo and hands one to me. I vehemently refuse, but when he persists I swallow it and gag. Thirty minutes in my jaw tightens, my heart rate soars, the skin all over my body is clammy and the walls pulsate, strengthening in colour like rocks under water. I'm swimming through a subterranean cave, no, a Matisse painting. Lipstick pink and pellucid green envelop me. I'm unsure where I am then it's obvious as I climb up the Atlas Mountains, the road a rock-strewn lunarscape with craters. It's amazing I can negotiate it, but I do, creating galaxies of dust as I go. I caress the relic of my student days as tenderness fills me. The empty space at my core is filled; the longing for home, deep as Odysseus's, assuaged. Floating weightless in the lightlands I feel myself glowing with a rapture that is almost radioactive. I'm here and I'm not, quivering on a threshold. *To be or not to be*, I say, astonished at my own erudition.

As red dawn light insinuates itself, he is still insinuated; for a brief, sweet spell before I exit his life we lie together, clammy, spent and at peace.

Netherworlds
(Gliding Planes, Parallel Worlds)

Threatening peace and psychic integration I'm exploring these states by more felicitous means, currently through Yoga. True, I struggle with *Supta Baddha Konasana;* rather than striking the Goddess Pose I fear I resemble a spatchcocked chicken. But I press on, aiming for the Vedic 'realm of light', a world beside this world wherein, says Jung, lies transformation - seemingly a source of controversy for aeons. By the Middle Ages 'occultists' were witches; Inquisitors were told *'It Has Come To Our Ears That By Sortileges And Charms They Cause Hailstorms, Tempests And Lightning To Blast Men And Beasts!'*

But centuries on, so my new neighbour Edward informs me, cutting edge science is *validating* parallel worlds - higher dimensions existing beyond space and time.

Egged on by Jung, I crack on. If, as it's been said, in altered states we can merge with anyone from this or another lifetime, or with seas and cyclones, algae, agate, amethyst, silver or gold; with tornadoes, volcanoes, diamonds, quartz crystals, silver, and gold – if consciousness can expand to encompass molecules, atoms, Brownian motions, subatomic particles and super-bright explosions of stars, with *everything* up to and including cosmic consciousness, there's definitely more to explore.

I serenely shoot for the moon. Even if I miss I'll land among stars.

Makeover Mind: Module 1

<u>Plane Earth</u>

I'm seeing stars from a Facetime blow courtesy of Marvin,
who, even as we speak, is wending his way across the Pond,
leaving his homeland intent on settling *here!* No more
Goodbyes, Good Lucks or Good Riddance after tortured
sessions either here or there.
(But thank heaven I can't prophesy where this will lead).

Consigning the thought to dissociative amnesia, and though
mired in resistance to my umpteenth course, balking at the
module *Jung and Freud,* I now perk up on learning a Sturm
und Drang of libidinous urges and libido theories, unruly
homosexual feelings and religious crushes with erotic
undertones raged like a bush fire, hurling the debris into
the void, provoking questions for a hundred years to come.

I take base pleasure in watching their impassioned friendship
descend into Shadow boxing, each declaring their own group
superior and activating each other's conflicts as fractures
appear on every fault line.

Freud, man of science and 'nothing but', declares religion a
form of neurosis.

'The need for religion must be sublimated' he implores Jung who, though given to the spirit world and self-induced trances, reluctantly begs Freud's forgiveness for his rampages of fantasy as Freud, with the fervour of an inquisitor, scolds:

'We must make an unshakable bulwark against the black tide of mud of occultism!'

They had me at erotic undertones. My mind expands to embrace my fellow travellers, my new best friends.

Invisible self meet invisible others! A brief empathy for the Umbraphobe Marvin surprises, as does the urge to rise Phoenix-like from the ashes, as did Carl and Sigmund before me.

Phoenix

Here's Freud as a child. If Sigismund Schlomo fights with a terrier's tenacity for his hard-won authority it's because of his early life: "*poverty, misery and extreme shabbiness!*" Despite which, sardined into a room rented from a drunken tinsmith on the medieval Ringstrasse with eight other children and his parents, he is praised by teachers and hated by school mates who make him cry. And if, despite being hounded by anti-Semitism raging through Europe, he graduates with honours and a double PhD, it is because he is bright and the favourite son of a mother so beloved he later bases a theory on it.

The Freuds move to Vienna before Jung is born, before Landtmann's opens fifteen minutes' walk away where Freud, leaving his consulting room promptly at one, drooling at the thought of asparagus and beef, will later walk through the stunning main hall to his seat at the back and in the golden hush and glow sit making notes. They move decades before inexorable forces bringing Jung to the city have gathered, and before the current Ringstrasse has risen phoenix-like into the crystal, marble and gold splendour of the Burgtheater, the Opera House, the fabulous University, from its crumbling medieval ramparts.

Freud, who reads Shakespeare throughout his life - *I am a Jew, if you prick us do we not bleed? If you poison us do we not die?* -

might later say of Vienna: opulent, lustrous, resplendent as he strolls around the modern Ringstrasse casting about for antiques, or stands blissed in front of Klimt's glimmering *Kiss*.

Hysteria, Mystery

Hysteria: 'A condition in women characterized by emotional outbursts with erotic undercurrents, faintness, irritability, a tendency to cause trouble'.

And here's Jung being born as Freud, our man of hard science, is undertaking research in Italy. His first microscopical study is on the testes of eels which he has the honour of discovering. 'No ordinary genitals', they say; 'they're the rudiments of psychoanalysis'.

Jung's mother meanwhile offers séances as others might tea, while his grandfather is not only Rector of Basel University but supreme leader of the Masonic Rosicrucians. As Jung junior is learning from this idol, Freud is crusading against rising occultism with hard, empirical facts - digressing slightly when he buys Cocaine, strictly for the purpose of research. As others inject it, ingest it, stuff it into every orifice for catarrh, masturbation and toothache, Freud repairs to France to study hysteria in women where he hangs over Paris at the top of Notre Dame, snorting Cocaine and drinking absinthe. Bemused by the look of Parisians he says: '*the people seem to me a different species from ourselves'.*

The following year is a haze. As young Jung in Switzerland is shoved to the ground by a bully causing him to faint whenever it's school time, Freud in Munich is enamoured of an Otolaryngologist. High on Cocaine his chum Wilhelm postulates a link between the nose and genitals - vindicated later when science shows nasal erectile tissue becoming engorged during sexual arousal, causing people to sneeze.

Sigmund tells Wilhelm he constantly and ardently longs to live near him, while praising himself for finding the key to restraining the power of the female sex. Just before Freud pulls away from Wilhelm in a rage of disappointment he writes: '*Rome is still distant; you know my Roman dreams*'.

Atchoo!!

They part in the bohemian metropolis at the very moment Jung goes to live there, immersing himself in the Munich Secession's erotic themes, rubbing shoulders with Klee, Kandinsky and Lenin who he spots playing billiards on the Schellingstrasse. Here is decadence and sin, exotic, lascivious art. Here are Freud and Wilhelm, severing their tie in the very hotel which will henceforth cause Sigmund to faint.

Who's Who
Losing her head

Feeling faintly ridiculous I've actually brought Marvin along - even though *he* is no friend. I see my wicked stepfather Philip in him, manipulative, bitter and cruel. But am I floundering around in a quagmire of counter-transference? Are 'Marve' and I characters in each other's scripts? Parts of my history and unconscious content are being reanimated - the game, as Lacan said is on, and I haven't got *a clue* which one is leading.

Barely able to practice I now count my patients on one hand – one finger - and it had to be Marvin!. Caught between worlds I've sought out seminars on Madame Blavatsky, past-life regression and quantum physics. Today, voices floating down over waves of adherents describe a quantum ocean where everything that has been, is, or will be, exists. I say *Beam me up Scottie* to Marvin. 'Science is the new language of spirituality', he replies, as though he's had an epiphany. He hasn't. I said that to him and I'd read it elsewhere. Alcohol has worsened his Wernicke-Korsakoff syndrome, rendering his memory a fog of bizarre fabrications. I make a mental note; *Cryptomnesia and Confabulation,* and I'm glad when Nefertiti takes over.

Now I'm sifting through my crowns, opting for the flat-topped blue. I annoy the sculptor throughout the sitting by reaching with my arm to adjust it. But I *love* the finished head; my lime-stone incarnation is beautiful, animated, life-like.

I step outside; my wilting retinue waft fans of scented feathers to shelter me from the sweltering heat as we walk where flowers red as fire flare like flames by my pleasure-lake, near my sunshade palace in my Egypt, my perfumed garden in the desert.

The Nefertiti Lift

Changing Face

<u>A parallel garden of delights</u>

We're happy and expectant we women. Someone's here for the tanning booth, another for the skin lightening treatment. Shots in the glossy brochure show hair with a fall like silk being crinkled, exuberant curls unravelled and tamed.

I'm buoyant, assured, on my black padded couch with the back part raised, my body at thirty degrees. Today I'm here for the needle. I've been using the cream; *'guaranteed to boost collagen, speed cell turnover and smooth out the skin'*, massaging it into my face as though performing a rite. No-one told me the vitamin A in it makes you susceptible to sun damage and as I bought it during that heatwave avoiding the sun has been hard.

With my face like a boiled crustacean I stopped the regimen, slathered on Extra Virgin and bolted off here for a Botox. I know the possible side-effects: problems swallowing, bad bladder control, trouble breathing, double vision. But gravity has caused my cheeks to go south; I'm told these wrinkle-relaxing injections will weaken the bands that are dragging them down and the opposing force of my facial muscles will pull them back up, creating the well-defined jawline of my alter.

There's no anaesthetic or numbing, just a rhythmic injecting, dabbing, injecting again. The needles don't hurt exactly, one point five on a scale of one to ten. There's swelling around the injection sites for around five minutes, I'm out of the chair in ten, back outside in an hour. I don't look like the Joker and no-one says a thing.

Things I Wish I'd known Before Botox:

Botulinum toxin is a neurotoxin, the most acutely toxic substance known. Botox requires *Black Box* labelling - the sternest warning a medication can carry and continue to stay on the market.

I still let them sell me more though. I'd been having a pedicure and was offered it but settled for a gynaecologist who offered it me on the side. I had my eyelids, lips and frown lines done. Weeks later, a friend who notices nothing noticed. I'd got a droopy eyelid, couldn't say my Ms for a month and now people have stopped laughing at my jokes because they can't tell from my face when I am kidding.

Projection

I must be kidding myself. When I try deciphering Marvin's art, he blasts my hostility which is actually *his* projected. Could shift possibly happen?

Conceding his penchant for all things frigid I'm showing images of Ice Age art - exquisite swimming reindeer carved from the tip of an elephant's tusk - when out of left field this from Marvin: *that the works show a very advanced consciousness!* I scrutinize my patient as might a young ornithologist a Great Crested Grebe, but there's still something chilling about him. Or am I projecting *my* animosity?

I dial up Jung who think yes. He's currently enamoured; she's dazzlingly bright and sexually preoccupied and it's troubling a 'civilised' society that stifles expression of the innermost self. Suppressing the green eyed goddess I link this to art as swiftly as Freud would to sex, rattling off parallels: the early Pharaohs who ruled as omnipotent God-kings, forcing artists to work to strict rules for millennia to come. Until, that is, the maverick Pharaoh manifests.

That Pharaoh; significant other of my incumbent other whose demise he will cause. He, a final straw that breaks Jung and Freud's ardent connection; he the monotheist who presciently deified the sun-disc as source and sustainer of creation - he who *liberated* art. Akhenaten's Amarna art is freed from Classical ideals in an age of sensual, expressive sculpture, lyrical poetry.

I show Marvin the limestone bust of my alter, its provenance as murky as Nefertiti's own. He sees austere beauty exuding the life force; I see a great divide closing.

Schadenfreude

When one chasm closes another one widens in your face. In a triumph of optimism over experience I seek Philip's advice on therapies I'm trying with Marvin, as scared of admitting my affinity with Jung as Jung his affinity with Nietzsche to the burghers of Basel.

Magnetically attracted to his rescue fish cowering in a tank in the shadow of his desk, Philip looks glum and no wonder: blue-green algae have coated the sides and camouflaged the Roman ruins.

'Siamese' he says in response to my request for help; 'won't eat plants or nip other fish'.

When he raises the spectre of my episodes I 'confess' as though by autosuggestion my fear of schism, a lack of feeling whole.

'The age-old fear endemic in females' he says, walking to the window. 'You lack the body part Freud called the more interesting component of the genitals'. He gestures to a man on the wrought-iron balcony opposite, returns to his desk and notes in my line of vision: *Denis asap, Lamb and Flag.*

The air is now stuffy and fetid, an unholy alliance of polish and fart. Pressing my fingernails into my palms, I repeat my request for advice.

'Freud was right', he says yawning; 'women add nothing of their own'.

As I abjectly shrink from the room, Philip's look of vindictive triumph chills me to my core.

Balancing Act

My big chill increases with the overnight frost. There's something Marve's not telling about Mom - about whom I know little except that she's dead, details of her entry to this altered state apparently being unmentionable.

At a loss - and as Freud once believed childhood sexual abuse to be endemic, I, a torn Jungian, find myself looking to *him* for clues. (Though Freud turned abruptly from making the theory his magnum opus to abandoning it completely, in fear no doubt that accused of en masse, the burghers of Vienna might sever part of his anatomy and remodel it as *Wiener Schnitzel*.)

Weary of schism, inner and outer, I'm bending the ear of *my* opposite Ed, pondering Freud's conflicting basic instincts; the erotic-creative and lust for destruction - just the terminology of which to my discomposure unleashes as though by Pavlovian conditioning something akin to his dogs' anticipatory salivation, (though looking to Ed might be barking up quite the wrong tree).

Back on message I contemplate poles as complementary unities and am beguiled by science's new world view; that quantum physics sees only one kind of stuff - light / matter

/ proto-consciousness - *an undivided whole as the nature of reality.* Warming to the science the male/ female reproductive organs come to mind - mirror forms that united create a most pleasing whole - without which methinks, we might as well be starfish or fungi.

Full circle to Marvin. Like a Woolly Mammoth suspended in a prison of ice, he too seems cut off from the life-force. Transcending disdain I feel a surge of warmth and compassion as my conscious mind and a better self briefly unite.

Changing Mind

Task for the day (begun evening): *Substance abuse.* For the purpose of research I light up my very last spliff. Circumnavigating my senses it activates the mesolimbic pathway – my brain's reward circuitry - causing an immediate jolt of intense pleasure. I regret it almost immediately. Nightly visitations, exciting though they be, are exhausting. I boot up, log on, sign in, give up, shut down and give in just as Ed decides to drop in. Could he sniff out weed through steel-clad concrete? 'No', he says, 'I was reading your mind; telepathy is now shown to be as factual as the link between a light switch and a lamp'.

I stare at his zits, the piercing eyes behind his bifocals; he censures my insolence. There's animus between us, but also a bond on some other level. We soon drift off in equal and opposite directions.

My thoughts turn to Marve who confounds, despite my substantial experience: I've explored communication through image, 'deepened my relationship with my art form', waded through clinical placements, emerged a state registered art therapist and now I'm ploughing through this e-Learning Masters delivered by a Centre for Neuropsychiatry. Despite trekking through hundreds of online lectures, numerous simulated patient interviews, novel e-Learning units and, improbably, quizzes; despite helping many people using talking therapies, cognitive behavioural and creativity therapies, I'm at an utter loss with Marvin whose hair loss has increased his distress. If anything, his Trichotillomania is worse – he no longer just pulls out his hair but *eats* it.

Still, I've come to believe we can rewire our brain by positive thoughts and conversely, replay negative ones at our peril. Despite which, I'm still passionately absorbed in key players in early western psychology: *Herr Doktors Jung und Freud*, thanks to whom I'm immersing myself in better forms of spacetime travel; burying myself in books.

FreudenJung

Buried in books I'm a child again, looking into a snow globe; through this lens I enter complete worlds.

Here's Sigmund, sucking deeply on his cigar, diffusing a pungent scent.

'I get aroused by that smell' he says, then points at a Zeppelin drifting across the sky. 'Phallic symbol', he chuckles, 'rising up in defiance of the laws of gravity!'

Carl sees the Zeppelin is distinctly cigar shaped.

'One of the first truly rigid airships', says Sigmund. Carl, still under the 'reverberating impact' of Freud's lecture, flushes and wafts at the acrid smoke.

'Spirit of my spirit', Sigmund says reverently; 'my heir and crown prince!'

Jung, though diffident, waxes lyrical, excited by science's new world view that cosmos and consciousness are one. Freud sternly interjects that the 'oceanic feeling of oneness' is no more than infantile terror on discovering itself separate from the mother's breast, but Jung continues, rhapsodic; writings on the spirit world ignite him.

'Natural philosophers' Freud says coldly, 'experiment with mesmerism to understand the forces of nature but do *not* embrace its spiritualist uses'! Then warmly: 'More Gugelhupf', he asks, enraptured by his dazzling colleague; 'Torte'?

Jung, in awe and with boundless admiration, takes a third large piece of Imperial Torte. The layers of dark chocolate and wafer-thin pastry in a thick ganache glaze remind him of man and woman; the earthy and the delicate, cloaked in a sensuous coverlet. He takes enormous bites, rolls his tongue across his moustache and laps at the creamy deposit.

But as Freud and Jung dig deep into each other's theories and psyches, are they setting in motion a breach as deep as the Kali Gandaki Gorge? One thing is sure; just one hour's walk away a glowering, violent teenage Hitler, possessed by tales of the hated 'other' and livid at rejection by the Fine Art Academy, is stalking the streets, casting a shadow over the city.

The Shadow falls

Umbra: 'shade / shadow'. The suffix 'elle': 'little'. Umbrella: 'little shadow'.
*'I have a little shadow that goes in and out with me,
though what can be the use of it is more than I can see.
It is very, very tall like me, from heels up to my head
and I see it jump before me when I jump into my bed'.

Battling down Harley Street barely perpendicular, I'm whipped by rain and a venomous wind, victim to the lunatic gyrations of my wilful umbrella.

As the unrelenting gale gathers force I perform involuntary contortions like someone doing the Saint Vitus dance. Arms thrown up and instantly dashed down, I'm forced to bow to my umbrella's demands in a wild choreography designed by it. Livid at this thing that has me in its power I wonder: *is Umbraphobia contagious?*

The elements prevail, rent the umbrella asunder. I dump it in a municipal bin, a broken thing, useless, and swamped by a deluge of weeping, surrender myself to the tempest.

*Robert Louis Stevenson 'The Golden Book of Poetry' (1947

)

Babylove

Tunnelling to the beginning of time: 2

Your sobs slow down but droplets of water continue to swell, gaining momentum to fall off your chin as though off the edge of a precipice.

Between thick metal bars fleeting white figures swirl by like phantoms. Your body aches with the longing for touch. Suddenly you're plucked up, fed, and quickly deposited back in your prison. Touch is not good. It causes the spread of infection.

Your mother doesn't come. Then one day you notice her shoes beneath an iron-framed curtain in the cavernous room. You scream. You hear your mother sobbing and your father's voice. But they mustn't let you see them, it will only upset you.

Soon it will be dark. They will come and inject you with a drug that can turn grass blue. The doctor wants to adopt you but no, you're going home! No more birthdays with harsh starched linen, ice-cold chamber pots, ear-splitting steel hitting hard cold tiles that throw hard cold light on cold glossy walls.

At home you won't let your mother put you down; you're more trouble than the others put together. No wonder they take you back.

Inside your head, neurons fire longing and hope but there are no receptors. You curl your small fingers around the bars rocking backwards and forwards, backwards and forwards. Each time you sleep you dream deeper. Now your beloved mother is holding you, gazing into your eyes causing indescribable joy.

You're a dreamer forever and ever.

Total Eclipse

With dreamlike illogicality I call on Philip, driven to excavate the past. On the way there, media scandals on every street corner blare our collective shadow: the 'other', a projection of everyone's darkness; whole nations demeaning others - a shadow puppet's grotesque performance played out on the world stage.

My mood drops further as I enter his office; my forehead contracts, my frown lines deepen like the number eleven engraved between my brows. As I iron them out with my thumb and finger Philip, spurs me on to 'that proper lift', offering to pay and handing me Denis's card.

'But you're *fundamentally* flawed' he says. 'A child such as you were, reintroduced after extended absence, causes disruption to the family dynamic'.

This is the dragon who guards my cave of self-knowledge. I struggle from his claws and bolt, fraught and disturbed as though from a nightmare, feeling disembodied, insubstantial as a shadow, uncertain I even exist.

Wounded surgeon
Tunnelling to the beginning of time: 3

Existential anxiety persists on recalling Philip and Denis reminiscing about the two of them slithering down in their seats during lectures then forcing themselves back into a sitting position and adopting an expression of interest. They were rascals back then.

Notes they used for paper planes as Hollins droned on.
'The tissues overlying facial bones are stratified, a bit like a club sandwich laid over undulating ground. The SMAS facelift comes about through adjusting these layers which are hoisted and taken up - as would a barber a section of hair - then cut to shorten and fixed with sutures'.

What Denis remembers:
Making a paper plane and sending it to Philip - an impressive flight that landed smoothly. As others took notes, Philip unfolded the aircraft, drew on the back and returned it.

The thing that turned Philip off surgery for good:
They tuned in to hear that a gliding plane that helps make facial expressions is crammed with nerves; that most injuries occur to the sensory nerves close to the jugular; that even if nerves continue to transmit electrical signals, all feeling is lost.

<u>Unfavourable outcomes.</u>

Hollins, a dead ringer for Philip's father who filled him with equal abhorrence, wheeled round and summarily sent them packing. In the corridor Denis, on seeing Philip's caricature of Kate, widely known to fancy him, winced; *'some men will put their penis where I wouldn't put my umbrella!',* burying the memory, along with thoughts of his father.

To Be Or Not To Be

Tunnelling to the beginning of time 4

Buried deep underground equidistant from Zurich and Vienna lies an atom smasher that can, when fired to super-energetic levels, detect parallel worlds in higher dimensions and shed light on dark matter. It's searching for something that's fizzing away in the quantum vacuum, popping into existence then breaking apart in a ten-sextillionth of a second.

This would be the Higgs boson, particle of a theoretical field that is hiding in plain sight throughout space; there's nowhere the field is not and will, if proven to exist, show matter to be insubstantial as a rainbow and all 'reality' virtual!

My fog of inertia lifts. I ask neighbour Ed to explain the Higgs and get particle-sex education.

'When two anti-fermions collide they exchange a virtual boson which emits a Higgs boson', he says. 'Proof of the Higgs would predict the couplings of bosons with each other as well as with quarks and leptons'.

I ask how they hope to prove its existence and get his father's political candidate speech:

'If they detect more decay signatures that *could have* been a Higgs than the Standard Model has predicted on the assumption there *is* no Higgs, this is strong evidence that it exists'.

The burning question is *do* they exist? Following experiments measured on quadrillion-byte computers running at two hundred teraflops a second, it seems - with more certainty than I feel about *my* existence - that they most probably do.

Here, There and Everywhere

It's a hazy Spring morning in Baton Rouge, a bitter cold noon in Goose Bay, a chilly afternoon in Basel, a sub-zero night in Vladivostok and a warm sultry dusk in Hangzhou when I discover the ability to look down on myself from the vantage point of infinity.

This field of light has a quality of eternity that despite its vastness brings a feeling of peace, the comfort of a bubble-bath, being mothered, coming home.

Zooming in closer I see myself everywhere at once, like a type of particle or God. Here I am, the 'pseudo-Wanderer' hanging over Chicago on the ninety sixth floor of John Hancock Tower looking down on the web of gold filigree below, imbibing a 'Windy City'; here I am in Zurich buying bolts of taffeta and silk and here in London, buying lotions in jars full of promise.

I'm a Higgs boson; all over the place and disintegrating with astonishing rapidity.

Denial: More Than a River

Those liddle lemon sponge rolls: *Ingredients*

Sugar.
Not good!

Egg, rice-flour, wheat-flour, glucose/fructose syrup, vegetable oil, water.
Mmm.. vegetables and water are good.

Humectant: Glycerol.
Glycerol? The stuff they use in Cryonics?

Moving on:
Mono and diglycerides of fatty acids, soya lecithin, sodium citrates, calcium citrates, disodium diphosphate, sodium bicarbonate; sodium acetate, sodium caseinate, sodium alginate; curcumin.
Oh dear!

No chemicals, artificial flavourings, preservatives or colours.
Phew!

Facebook: Virtually Yours

Weaning myself off my Newsfeed I take tea and cake with Jung; I've found an excellent therapist in him, though some of his insights are difficult to swallow. True, my cowardice *is* hard to refute. Even so. Even though we've had very chummy meetings since he poked me - (when I found it on my Homepage I immediately poked back) – I've toyed with 'unfriending without offending', at the very least unfollowing, but I've rallied. His latest bitter pill is that some of my difficulties stem from repressing the Wanderer, causing me to live out its shadow - which I can't help thinking rings true.

What I now realise:

- I'm Shadow-possessed, standing in my own light, living below my own level.
- I'm ontologically insecure, unsure of my actual *beingness*.
- I stopped eating octopus on discovering they can do Lego.

Whatever to do?
'Think Descartes', prompts Jung, adding that though we *are* physical beings we also have a helper that exists distinct. This

could be true. I increasingly find my conscious mind influenced by some 'other' that spurs me to do what I dare not.

www.collectiveunconscious.com

Jung has swung to his gloomy mode. I recount my dream all the same, in which I'm thundering across desert sands on a beast, half-man, half-horse. On one hand it's alien and terrifying, on the other it feels like a part of me. I'm Queen of the desert astride him; his muscles beneath me cause a sensation I blush to describe that comes, as the dream does, to a juddering, tumultuous halt.

Jung brightens. The feminine and masculine aspects of the psyche - a notion he exhumed from Egyptian antiquity! He acknowledges my interest before turning away, distracted by the cover of a magazine showing an asexual colossus from the National Museum in Cairo. It's Pharaoh Akhenaten and Queen Nefertiti as one!

As he's absorbing this 'coincidence' a scarab beetle, Egyptian symbol of the sun god, flies straight at the window and beats its wings in an act of gratuitous synchronicity.

Now he's ablaze. The desert of my psyche contains untold buried treasure; I must first make conscious the Shadow and the Animus - archetypes of the collective unconscious. This will be my apprentice-piece. But undertaking the Hero's Journey, 'the path of psychological growth that lies at the heart of religions' - *that* will be my masterpiece, he says with more faith than foresight.

PART THREE
FUSION

The Hero's Journey

3 a.m. Lurched out of sleep I lie tense, motionless, pounding, on a moulded unyielding surface with straps and buckles hurting my head. In the harsh, cold light, blasts of cold air gush forth as a weird metallic thing laced about with fat writhing flexes comes looming towards me, whirring and screaming its deafening roar.
Acid rises in my gullet, pain stabs my chest and jaw.

As consciousness grows relief floods in. I register the object as a floor polisher smacking against the seating I'm lying on. My feet, stuffed into striped paper bags for warmth bring an embarrassed flush to my face that smoulders in polished chrome rails and gleaming plate-glass as I drag my rucksack across the North terminal floor.

By five a.m. I'm boarding the plane as nuclear families explode around me; by afternoon I'm on the island in a stifling surgery where blue-bottles suck my salt moisture. An old man strides over, whacks my leg smartly with a rolled-up paper and grinning triumphantly through toothless gaps, points to dead flies on the floor.

I escape with nothing more contagious than glee and relief

at having something antacid can cure; I was sick with the fear of travelling alone. Later I sit at a wonky-legged table sipping Ouzo, watching crimson sunset tints seep over the shimmering, metallic-blue sea.

Archetypal Hero

Scouring winds batter the dark green shutters as I, curled in a foetal ball on the bed, fight residual panic and try to catch up on sleep.

I drag myself to the bathroom and on my return find to my horror an enormous bee like a small contented cat where I've just been lying; my systolic and diastolic rates bounce over and below the bar like musical notations.

As the umbrella to Marvin, this bee is to me. But I dimly see that this is *a test*.

Thinking quickly and laterally I grab a fridge shelf and tumbler and move stealthily towards the bed. Expecting to be spotted, homed in on and punctured, envisioning death by anaphylactic shock at any second, I cover the killer with the glass. Miraculously I can wiggle the shelf underneath it because of the flexible mattress.

This arrangement I carry outside, set it with the now crazed bee on the balcony table, grab a broom handle - whose length on the time-space continuum is how long I have to escape - and knock over the glass with a thunderous crash, confusing the bee for the split second needed.

Turning tail I rush back inside, slamming the doors, swivelling the brass hinges to the locked position as the bee soars up to the deep blue yonder.

Stealthily peering beyond shattered glass, feeling becalmed as the bay, I step out in late sunlight and sit with my elbows resting on the cool metal table till the palm-fringed beach and the tiny islands dissolve in the fading light.

Island of Eros

With fading resolve I panic as we head up a towering mountain that plunges in serpentine drops to the sea. As we go ever higher, his car spluttering, my courage plummeting, the air is pungent with pine and jasmine; olive trees flicker dull silver. High, high up in their midst, planted in earth that is fierce ferrous red, is an old stone farmhouse smothered by blooms the colour of blood. *His habitat; not mine.*

I'm deeply unsure I still feel the 'reciprocal influence of life energy' towards *this* old beau.

Relief floods in when his mother appears, scraping three wooden chairs over ornate tiles dotted in the concrete and, nudging him, tells him to take me for mezze.

The sun beats down in waves of palpable heat; black-clad, weather-beaten figures beat olive trees with sticks; goats nibble, filling with the cheese he's feeding me.

'Luscious', I tell him.

Down the steps the sun lights up the turquoise lake; waves flop and lap the sand. In the water happy, sun-toasted bodies are bobbing and floating. Their gladness transmits; I'm serene, calm.

The sky and sea become luminous. As we walk up the

mountain the sun sinks deeper, fiery red creeps up like a blush. Bare legged we continue, skimming harsh bark as our hips press close in the comfortable dark. At the top, the stars and moon hang over the Aegean in a sky as black as squid ink; far below, silver-laced waves whisper to shore on black satin water and chinkle on pebbles in rhythmic succession. It's night on the island of Eros.

New York New Year

London - a century after Carl and Sigmund set sail for America to spread the new creed. I'm dolefully dead-heading Poinsettias when I hear from the ruler of the gate of my dreams, god of athletes and edible roots, entity of bland cunning, igniter of fire, who asks; what would I wish for?
Too late, I tell him, the New York Matisse retrospective is sold out. But he is intent.

New York We reconvene days later at a Times Square hotel. The gleaming brass gates of the elevator part; going up. And up. It's the Penthouse suite - views of Manhattan at a hundred and eighty degrees! We head straight out to queue for cancellations. It is bitterly cold. As our story spreads down the line like wildfire a MOMA staff member winkles us out: did we _really_ fly from Europe without tickets? He tells us to meet him after closing, sounding very expensive.

At lunch my Greek god is obsessed with the waitress and gives her his card; we still go back and make love before heading to our assignation where MOMA-man unlocks the gallery and ushers us in. It is, as Freud said of his New York visit, 'the realisation of an incredible dream'. _We alone_ view delectable work sent from Paris, London and Russia with love. MOMA-man won't accept a dollar.

Next morning, check out. Later at JFK he helps a woman from her cab, holding her hand like Prince Charming assisting Cinderella and offering her a room in his house if she's ever in Greece. I turn and leave, waving Hermes *goodbye!* His bewildered face turns back to me all the way to the stargate. As the pumpkin takes off I'm exalted with bravery, daring to dream a new dream- an impulse detour via Chicago!

Fading Faculties, Fainting Goats

My last time in the Windy City followed a road trip of mythical significance.

I'd passed homeland security – *(I do / do not bring disease agents, cell-cultures, snails or soil)* and we'd laughed or gasped from East to Midwest, my Russian-doll baby / small child / magnificent grown woman and I. *She* in the driving seat, me with the map. We drank Gin in log cabins where earth-smelling mountain towns stream through the Catskills with film-set facades; on trails perpendicular we climbed to Bald Knob - with no little ribald remarking!

My navigating skills being not what they were, we searched on in the gloom where mountains loom over forests for Robert Frost's birthplace; we'd taken the road less travelled too often. By moonlight she read from a hand-crafted sign, 'Fainting goats, and all kinds of gifts'. I squinted helpfully: *farting goats*? Needing neither and still off course we pressed on to Chicago.

Who was mother in that rite of passage? She'd packed a powder-blue fleece to warm me; I bought a seven-dollar reflexology kit and pummelled her feet in specified places, connected it said, to the pelvis.

A lasting image of me and my daughter on the forecourt of

Comfort Inn: we hugged crushing goodbyes and as Moms are wont, I pointed to her feet: 'now you know where your ovaries are don't you darling?'

****

Shifting through space-time back to JFK, impenetrable announcements blare out, bringing me crashing to earth. As a boisterous family bears down I slap my bag on the seat beside me forming a barricade; I am nasty with longing.

Journal: War and Peace

Lake Michigan, noon. I hobble, deporting self awkwardly, dodging goose shit. Canadian geese won't leave, nothing Homeland Security can do. I bus down to atelier for vouchers leaving barely a fistful of dollars.

To Cultural Centre for Handel free-gratis. Run right into Kenneth, we hug and walk by the shape-shifting lake up to Oak and iconic, beacon-like John Hancock Tower; lie on the sea wall sun-flushed. My favourite blue vest-top barely meets my skirt, revealing flesh which he fingers lightly. We move on in utter serenity.

Treat K to *Ballaké Sissoko* on Kora / Paciugo's for late night gelati. If I was remiss in mentioning my ex, he was his Colonoscopy. We didn't have the wit to woo.

No response from K re request to borrow saw, a flimsy opening for him to call round. Write again, putting Saw Point in the subject line; go painting; splash clashing colour in slashing, gestural strokes. Repair to Caribou Coffee with defiant pain-au-raisin from House of Fine Chocolate, get numbness in lumbar from hard wooden chair.

Time to move on and I must. Have never done New York *alone*; fear being held up at knife point and forced to eat cream cheese with lox on a bagel.

To New York on spoils from my paintings; am a Fauve apparently. Bum cheeks killing me; declare high wooden chair in *Au Bon Pain* at La Guardia a pain in the ass but framed by the Belle Epoque mirror my face an emoticon, mouth curved upwards.

Melting pot

To the world's loveliest station according to Travel and Leisure, swept up by a tide in the gloom of the platform and thrown down in the splendour of Grand Central's cavernous main concourse. Beneath the lustrous astronomical ceiling with its quirky reversed constellations – a simple mistake according to some, to others how the sky looks to God – I send up a prayer.

Striding about apparently with purpose I tag onto ant-like columns surging this way and that through the ornate labyrinth then step out onto 42nd struggling not to look like prey. I am calcified with fear. Here the whole world converges; a playwright called it the Melting Pot, predicting with more optimism than occult vision that pole and equator, crescent and cross would be 'fused by the great Alchemist with purging flames'.

One October 17th at 7:46 a.m. Eastern, somewhere along that mythical road trip, the population hit three-hundred million. It's been said the Bush administration, 'while not playing down the milestone' wouldn't be marking it with cake and punch. The next president declares the 'patchwork heritage' a strength not a weakness. 'We've emerged from the dark days strong and united' he says, with more hope than foresight.

Propelling myself into the patchwork heritage I make for the crashing Atlantic at the toe of Manhattan before heading back north - now side-stepping bits of the twelve thousand tons of garbage filling six hundred trucks each morning, now inching towards the Met where fragments depicting Nefertiti's life send me into the stratosphere, up there with the gods.

Light

*Face that lights my face**

<u>Met Opera, Broadway; up in the gods</u>
With the flick of a switch I'm *bitter,* despite the thrill of stumbling on this performance. I stood hours in the cold for a miserable ticket, now here I am, kneeling and craning.

The curtain rises on a humongous crimson sun, backlighting a mysterious figure: Akhenaten!

Akhenaten: 'The old order fades, a new age dawns, a new power rises. Behold, the sun!'

Now, as suddenly, I'm vibrating high, transported by Glass's operatic portrait of Pharaoh.
I set about raising my frequency *higher,* shooting for the realm where 'streams of electro-magnetic radiation dance between particle and wave', according to mystical scientist Bohm — aka the Zero Point Field / the realm of Nirvana that seems as keen to be known as we are tanatalised by it.
I'm lead to believe that while *it* vibrates up there, even if mortals could manage it, and we can't, *we wouldn't stay physical,* but I aim to get as near as I can without undergoing teleportation.

Hovering spectrally between there and the earthbound, with excruciating pain in my knees, I give way to the bliss that haunting strains can evoke - like this solar-powered, mesmerizing chanting in ancient Egyptian that I know will insulate against glacial temps that await.

'Face that lights my face, you pour consciousness into the particles I am'. Rumi, Sufi poet

Lead us not

<u>Marve's pied-a-terre, the Bronx. (Not far from Fordham, where Jung presented his Magnum Opus).</u>

Possessed by the spirit of my alter and suffering a relapse I light some Egyptian Musk and stick it in the Tutankhamen incense burner. The search is still on for Akhenaten.

I drowsily dab on some perfume, crayon kohl round my eyes and begin my homespun invocation, dancing in front of the full-length mirror. Pungent smoke permeates the bedroom, causing a stinging in my glittering eyes.

The sultry night deepens; she still isn't here. I open the door and swing it on its hinges, fanning the room, then flop on the bed with my arms splayed out as though I'm directing traffic.

I wake feeling chilly way before dawn to a presence in the room. I watch her perform those erotic gyrations, swinging her heavy blue wig; she rotates her hips as though she's dug out my Hula-Hoop from somewhere.

I stagger to my feet and dance alongside her, eyes down and side-ways, copying each move. What *is* peculiar is, search as I might, I see neither hide nor hair nor trace of her in the mirror.

Dawn breaks. I gaze out looking East, worshipping the sunrise as she would. On a whim I rush out and take a cab south. In rose-tinted light I glimpse the Statue of Liberty rising from the water like Botticelli's Venus and the One World Trade Centre risen from the ashes of where the twin towers had once stood, helping me shake off benumbing nocturnal travels.

Death of a Star

Upper East Side; bone-chilling cold.
Fingers numbly shedding thick woollen layers I enter the arty-party thrown in my honour. Between insipid nibbles and lurid libations we play an on-trend game of charades. Gesticulations exhausted, the challenger points to me in my little black dress, snug as a Mummy's wrappings, as the code-cracking clue.

Et voilà, *Blackstar!* This takes me abruptly back to a sombre moment. As I was leaving the gourmet 'Vinegar Factory' with a single slice of Smithfield Ham I could formerly only dream of devouring, Facebook spread the word that David Bowie, like his sloughed-off alter Ziggy Stardust, had shuffled off his mortal coil within days of the launch of *'Blackstar'* on which he's singing "Look up here, I'm in heaven".

In my introspective state this causes me to ruminate on what Bowie referred to as *'something greater than ourselves,* aka the *'larger being or mind'* surmised by a rubber company boss turned evangelist in a book found on another deified musician on *his* passing - the sensual, soulful man with the blue suede shoes who half a billion fans and the wheels of commerce have made a Blue Giant, light years away but incandescently present.

Back on terra firma, I feed Marve's neighbour's cat some of the gourmet ham to lure it into its basket. The tiger-clawed meanie morphs into a cutie on the way to the vet's, its mind and body, like mine for the moment, appeased.

But while I'm getting a sense that something *good* is advancing through the ether, I'm possessed of the notion it won't be unless my brain gets rewired and vow to cast out my schism.

Divide

Starbucks 125th remembering …

<u>America:</u>
After practicing defence against Grizzlies, rattle snakes and crazy wild turkey my nearest and dearest walk thousands of miles of the Continental Divide Trail from Mexico to Montana.

<u>Cornwall:</u>
My longest-standing friend in her attic bedroom; silks and taffetas, nets and satins fall like rainbows around her as she fades through colours like a dying leaf. She turns her head to her partner then to her ex as Paul harangues Mark to sign over the house because, he says, Rube could die any day now. Mortified I protest; Paul orders me to leave and Rube concurs, smiling as though at a child who wouldn't understand. And I don't.

I shrink away past the gabled window framing sky and sea where dolphin shapes still traced in Christmas lights bob with the waves in the bay; get drenched as I walk to the train. The Riviera Express curls out; Mount's Bay in its grey veil of rain spirals away telescopically. Newlyn lighthouse, Penzance snail-shaped church, framed by my window fly by, as finished a picture as the vivid silk pouches of Jasmine and candles Rube painstakingly makes me before she dies.

London:

My daughter arrives, fresh from the Trail. Next day we watch a disaster movie on TV - Manhattan's twin towers spewing mushroom clouds like volcanic ash; monstrous billows of choking smoke and flames like a cartoon *Bham!*

My gut reaction is spontaneous and powerful: the only hope for our planet, be it ever so faint, is to seek *out there* in the universe, find a new 'other'. That's what it would take to close the divide.

Star Wars, Tardigrades

Here in the deep blue yonder we're optimistic, we 'aliens'. Star Wars, incidentally, got it wrong. Like your earthbound Waterbears from the phylum Tardigrade - which you've managed to find from the high Himalayas to the ocean's deep, from Pole to Equator in lichens and mosses, marine or freshwater sediments, we're Polyextremophiles.

We can withstand a hundred degrees Centigrade of heat, zero Kelvin, a thousand GY of radiation, the vacuum of space and decades without water (which is why you haven't looked here and found us).

We expect you to prevail when we see you engaging the pumping organ that keeps you alive to save fruit-eating birds and omnivores, herbivores and fish-eating species from extinction. And you've accomplished staggering feats; nuclear fission for one.

But you're more likely to deploy the eighty million kilojoules released from the fission of Isotope 235U on blowing each other to smithereens than on powering your lives. That's despite the fact you're all exactly alike: four limbs, a torso, and a head that you use to develop these strategies.

It all hangs in the balance. Will the dynamic between good and evil propel life forward on Earth? Or will you annihilate yourselves, leaving only a burnt-out planet as your footprint in space and us feeling desolate once more?

Barack Hussein Obama

… a man bent on *averting* an incinerated planet who was born in Hawaii; a tough call but someone had to do it.

Before the hoped-for new dawn of that night on Lake Mich, before the Obamarama came to town, from one of those closets where skeletons are kept jumped an article headed by a photo of 'Barry' looking vaguely like Elvis - another heartthrob who fused black and white. The article let the world know that as a student Barry had indulged in Ganga, alcohol and sometimes Cocaine - done, he averred, to help numb confusion about his identity as well as the thoughts of Nietzsche and Freud he'd waded through during his sophomore year.

As adept at getting all bases covered as the Cubs, Obama defused the incendiary device; the skeleton stepped out and faded into night before it could explode in a conflagration of blinding white flash bulbs as he fought his presidential campaign

Exuding incalculable volumes of charisma, garnering the black vote, the white vote, the grey vote, the gay vote, the every which way vote, he was inaugurated 44th president, the first African-American to hold office. From every sector the masses cheered with a swooning devotion normally reserved for pop royalty.

On that freezing January night in Chicago, on a glittering outdoor stage in Grant Park, exaltation insulated thousands of us from biting winds blowing in off the Lake. The inaugural address lit fires of zeal in hearts from each side of the polar divide as he says with more hope than hindsight: *The old hatreds shall someday pass, the lines of tribe shall soon dissolve, our common humanity shall reveal itself*.

Gravitational Embrace

<u>Vienna</u>:
Here's Freud at 19 Berggasse, trying to bind *his* tribe - unruly
disciples he thinks lack the intellect, passion and *brilliance* of
Jung.

<u>Zurich</u>:
As an ill-wind whips the lake into turbulent waves Jung is
agitated too; he's preparing to go to Amsterdam to present
the teachings of Freud who hopes Jung as 'the other' will be
spared what he would have met with. He tells Jung, 'All
hearts open to you, there's something in *me* that people find
repellent'.

<u>Amsterdam</u>:
In the Congress, as the 'filthy unscrupulous delegates'
denigrate anyone of Freudian persuasion, Jung feels in need
of a bath.

<u>Annenheim</u>:
The fire flickers red, bathing Freud in a peppery light; he
clips a cigar with a tough steel cutter and winces. As he rolls
it between thumb and finger exquisite sensations course
through him - it fits his hand as snugly as a Viennese
sausage in a roll. He retires to his room and takes up a pencil.

Damn! Is there *nothing* that doesn't have sexual connotations? When he thinks about it, no there isn't. The list is endless: objects from which water flows, those that penetrate or extend, taps, watering cans, hanging lamps, spears, umbrellas - up to and including this damned extensible pencil!

He has a sudden urge to draft a missive to Jung: '*Your letters have become a necessity. Please write!*'

Zurich:

Jung, happy to have been fighting for a good and honourable man rejoices in Freud's riches, insisting he lives from the crumbs that fall from his table.

Annenheim:

'No, no!' Freud extolls, relieved. 'It's *your* work makes *me* feel impoverished. It is cowardly', he writes, 'that I was in the Tyrol picking mushrooms and bathing in this peaceful Carinthian lake'.

Down, Derry-Down

Waves lap the lakeshore as Carl drafts a note to Sigmund, on whom he showers accolades like 'hero' and 'demi-god', before remarking prosaically that there are faeces all over the Burghölzli.

Soon though, dropping through the layers of his mind, he finds himself descending the steps to the Barfüsserplatz; it's noon and fiercely hot. As he floats above Basel a childhood dream pushes up like a ghost of Christmas past, of his mother who has two personalities as he does. He's on the dimly lit landing of their home; the door of his mother's room opens. Out she's stepping, translucent as a jelly fish, when her head detaches and floats in front of her …

Next up; the Munster is towering above him, an ornate construction of fairy tale and myth, when a giant turd drops from the heavens and razes it to the ground!

A magnificent edifice felled by a turd? What *can* this all mean?

Returning from the deep, he has the unwelcome thought that, as Freud sends him off to do his dirty work, surely he's entitled to doubt whether sexuality is the 'mother of *all* feelings' - not only one aspect, however important?

Struggling with the need to agree and disagree he ends his

letter to Sigmund loyally, saying that certainly, he's *seen* only sexual complexes, but he can't help noticing his new ambivalence.

Is the shit about to hit the fan?

Home

<u>London Heathrow.</u>
With hair like a cowpat and half dead from the red-eye I stumble through the morass with no sense of coming home.

<u>Between worlds.</u>
Slumped damp and crumpled, heading south-west. In the train's double-glazed window I see a double image of myself, torn between tribe and the Global Village in a world-in-waiting for peace that transcends divisions.

Timeless scenes are framed and fly by. Gliding barges lit with flowers on dark canals; faded brick cottages in the hazy green fields of my childhood, triggering an ache for those days, for my mother and those jewel-like times, fine and rare, when I had her to myself as the others revelled in the great outdoors on sledges made from old prams.

Beneath this, an *archaic* longing, deeper than a Superdeep Borehole.

<u>Cornwall.</u>
Dragging my bags; picking up my car. It makes a weird noise as I drive the few miles to the cottage conceded by Giles in the spoils of war, but soon I'm out on the headland.

Looking up through the black-green pines I feel suddenly alive; this is *known*. I'm at one with undulating hills like gentle

95

beasts, escarpments dropping softly to sea; warm-yellow rooftops, grey slate with whitewash, dark-green, moss-green resonate deeply. *As did upstate New York. Schunemunk; Matteawan a land imbued with the spirit of the ancients.*

My world needs Jung to decode it.

At the head of the estuary Bodmin rises. The sunset erupting in turquoise and shocking-pink tones, bathing the moor stretching back as far as the eye can see till it becomes one with the sky, fills me with rare contentment.

Divine Homesickness

Waves of contentment lap over me as I trip up the lane; I halt abruptly. At my window are decorative textiles in place of my slatted wood blinds. My legs turn to jelly on the thousand-mile walk to my door. My key doesn't fit; I ring the bell and a woman answers. She can't understand what I'm saying but beckons me in.

I'm shivering but my 'hostess' is warm towards me. She helps me to a seat, concerned I might fall. I look around mesmerised, want to protest but exhaustion prevents it. I accept a little food and water.

This is *my* house, changed beyond recognition. There's nothing of my identity *except* - on the front room wall - my meditation poster; a smokey-grey circle, symbol of *akasha* – a Sanskrit word for essence, or our connection to those who 'vibrate with the same harmonics' - a *true* homecoming, which I now unexpectedly feel.

As Freud said to Einstein: 'The bond of identification gives the feeling of community'.

Even as I long for my real home and family I fall into a routine with my new soulmates. The women of the house are delightful, elegant as Sanskrit itself: *karma, nirvana, saree* - meaning 'strip of cloth' – hardly conjuring the whole nine yards they're gracefully swathed in. These will-o'-the-wisps, slight as ladies in a Malwa painting awaiting with passionate longing their musical prince, inspire me to a full-costume portrait. I gaily lay in the ancient colours: turmeric, indigo, rose-madder.

I wake up absolutely drenched.

In the Balance

Bent on dodging a drenching I step out jauntily, heading for rocks that tumble from the slung back headland where razor-sharp layers of shale and slate jut up like triangular sandwiches.

Tightrope walking the jagged spine, arms out for balance, sandals dangling from hands, I leap back smartly and examine my foot. Blood drips into a rock pool; I watch it disperse, making pink water.

On the shoreline miniature figures gambol and dive like contented dolphins. The sea is pale like a lime green Daiquiri; lights dart across it, shooting and fading like sparklers. But as the sky turns leaden and colour disappears like a cinematic fade out, my mood darkens with it. A deluge sets in and soon I'm lashed by it, drenched.

I squelch back to my car. As rain crashes down the landscape turns white, departing cars skim water like hovercraft. I sit with a towel on my waterlogged-legginged knee till sea and cliffs, the colour of cement, emerge from the fog and rain.

When the pelting on my roof becomes less deafening I open the window a fraction as cautious as Noah, step out and scale the slimy route up to the crumbling cliff, sticking close to the edge of the coastal path.

Heather bees zizz and bomb me, causing me to stumble. I press on, climb a stile and clutch an electric fence, but nothing happens.

Peeling back layers, I reach for memories before they fade with the dying light.

Peels

Things I wish I'd known before Peels.

The effects of chemical peels on the skin are like taking the peel off a lychee and revealing its moist tender core, producing a weeping effect, similar to scraping a knee.
The treatment also exposes nerve endings; this may be uncomfortable but generally heals within days. Time-release systems can reduce discomfort until new skin forms.

Alpha Hydroxy Acids – AHAS – are the mildest for use in facial peels and can be bought over the counter, or for higher concentrations, is salons and spas.

Trichloroacetic Acid is a _much more_ powerful chemical. As well as being used in facials it also kills genital warts.

Phenol peels are uber strong, the most dangerous peels on the market; they sometimes leave skin looking similar to that of the victims of burns.

'Beauty is rarely achieved without pain'.

Although treated areas may be red, tender, sore or crusty with oozing and scabbing, the whole procedure can take less time than watching a sitcom.

In just a few weeks - at the most in months - you may feel comfortable in public again.

Multiple peels are often required to make your skin young and fresh.

Patients with heart problems are not good candidates for phenol peels.

Getting Rewired

Heart in mouth I part slatted blinds and see to my horror a thing like a Tardis swing by. It flies through the air with the greatest of ease like a heavy brass weight on a slender string light-pull, coming to rest in the garden.

A *carsey* has landed, next to my Winter-flowering Cherry. With it comes the total devastation. Dust changes my world like the first fall of snow. Re-papered walls get hacked, floors get ripped up, my Safavid *trompe-l'oeil* carpet gets trashed. Archaic withered cabling, ancient speckled pipework, centuries of dust, dead mice and grime beyond telling are unsuspected guests in my house.

One Tuesday the electrician's leg brushes mine in the kitchen. We beam at each other. Electric storms perform thunder clashes and lightning flashes in synaptic clefts of my brain; lust peptides rush to sites all over my body.

On Wednesday, poking through the attic trapdoor like someone being sawn in half, he hands me a newspaper clipping. It's an image of *him*; here's Mark my spark with a stark white face putting *two* burning torches down his throat.

On the day the Portaloo gets airlifted out Mark loads his M. reg. Escort; crams 'fishing' rods, drills, reels of cable, cable-strippers and infinitely borrowable screwdrivers in. I'm carrying his Saxophone, feeling happy, wondering if it's an illusion but I'm pretty certain it's not.

'There's a trick', he tells me, 'to fire eating: pain, and blisters on tongue, lips and throat. It takes years to get back to normal'.

He looks normal to me as I stare at his sensuous lips.

Vermillion Zone

Lips are soft and tactile and extremely sensitive due to numerous sensory nerve endings.

They are the transition point between facial skin and the mucous membrane inside the mouth, which is also *highly* sensitive. They're known as the Vermilion Zone because of the abundance of blood vessels in the skin. Oral Sphincters allow stretching of the circular fibres around the lips while contracting them makes a funnel, enabling them to be used for sucking and exploring objects.

Kiss

♥ Master work and treasure, the bust of Queen
Nefertiti, is displayed to great adulation at the
Neues Museum in Berlin on the centenary of her
rising and rebirth. As my alter-ego resurfaces I feel
a thawing of the permafrost hardening my heart.

♥ Klimt's opulent painting The Kiss is on show in
Vienna in an exhibition entitled Expectation and
Fulfilment. Its golden surface belies a darker
subtext evident in the rapacious yearning of the
man and the swooning submission of the woman.

♥ Up in the heliosphere supersonic winds abruptly
drop, the magnetic field ramps up. As a result of
reciprocal influence highly charged particles are
being drawn to each other - a commingling of the
known with the unknown.

♥ Not far from Stonehenge, whose altar, portal and
station stones show consideration of
solar alignments, a meeting of lips occurs.
Beginning with an awkward embrace connected
only at the shoulders like conjoined candy canes or
a couple of bent figures by Lowry, it causes effects

on the scale of earthquakes, volcanoes and the raising of mountains. Transcending sleight-of-hand and sniping, it has the power of an electrical charge, igniting fire at my core.

♥ Electrical charge has a tendency to spread over a conducting surface and may be transferred between bodies by direct contact.

Divine

Divine longing is the longing for oneness, completeness. Sexual longing is life's longing for itself. They are prodigious forces.

Contraction and expansion are prodigious forces. White hot temperatures melt rock in the core of the earth, causing it to expand. Volcanoes expel the lava as convulsively as a contracting womb expelling its newborn.

Gravity is a powerful force, though a pulsating star can force radiation outwards at a power exceeding the gravitational pull inwards, causing its size to expand, its temperature to rise, its luminosity to dazzle.

Friction, though not a fundamental force, arises from the electromagnetic force between charged particles in two contacting surfaces; it is the force resisting the motion of these surfaces sliding against each other. Lubricated friction occurs where a fluid separates the surfaces, converting kinetic energy to heat.

Contraction and expansion can cause a peak sensation of intense pleasure, inducing altered states.

I am a pulsating star, at one with the forces of nature. Heat radiating from me defies the pull of gravity; my temperature rises and falls; expansion and contraction consume me. I am a Supergiant, twice as light as the sun.

****

A supergiant's luminosity is rare and short-lived. Will this happiness be as fleeting?

PART FOUR
FISSION

Fleeting moments

I'm incandescent, emitting light, when, like an all-out total eclipse, your message casts a shadow, darkening my world, hitting its mark with the force of a thousand-pound forged steel wrecking ball.

My whole being recoils with loss; my body pumps out sobs like bellows forcing out air, washing away ancient pain mingled with this recent.

After the shock, saltwater falling, tissues scattered like wet confetti, my face as puffy as that time in Greece after sleeping on the beach and mosquitos had feasted on the flesh of my sleeping eye lids. Tears and snot slurry down my face. Electric kisses, kissing all night; from dusk till dawn your razor-sharp stubble stripped skin from my chin to a livid, festering wound.

Another whole bottle last night; awoke around three, made coffee at six, puked up at six-ten. Immersed myself in an ambient, amniotic bath. You bruised my breast with a crushing hug; a huge, black-yellow mark. You'll no longer be giving me those crushing hugs. I am bruised beyond telling.

Embers

I hug the wheel, coaxing my car. In the rear-view mirror I see red-rimmed eyes; with a struggle I see through the rain-lashed rear window traffic right up to the skyline.

It's late when I get back to the cottage, but soon I'm ensconced, staring out at the rain-shrouded bay. Propped up aloft against plumped up pillows, enshrined in a mocking heart-shaped arrangement of lights, I put myself to sleep with a shot of antacid and a Zinfandel chaser.

Next day a set change. The hot sea is glittering like fragments of mirror; good ships Mollyhawk, Jade and Quiver wobble on the swell. Stumbling down the beach I swim out till my chilled pimpled skin is like peel. I ought to turn back but swim on; in a moment of terror I fear being dragged out to sea; imagine jelly-fish will gather and clamp themselves to me, my flailing limbs causing phosphorescent sparks in the darkness.

Expending all strength I flip over, facing another world. Blood-red colour sculpting itself over the waves reminds me of my dress, a Thirties relic from Portobello; the magnificent red skirt over ripples of black net pushed up to my thighs; pleasure weakening my limbs.

With a monumental effort I struggle for shore. The tide turns, assisting my effort, helping me in.

Down by the jetty the sunset is stage-lighting regiments of boats, the harboured sea is like foil. Across the estuary the headland seems lit from within, its lights burn like embers. The sun's last rays shoot gold radii of light, meeting at the point where I stand, in this fleeing moment, serene.

Meltdown

Serenity fades. I lose my bearings on the way to the glass making workshop; the man from the store helps me out, seeming heroic through the filter of my longing. As he waves me off I suffer separation anxiety and project us into a dull but comforting marriage with him already on a diet.

But there's a glass wall between me and a steady life. As to what people think, I know the Oxford Concise definition verbatim. '*Possessed by a foolish, extravagant passion*'.

I trudge up the hill where vivid geraniums spill and cavort across whitewash and slate. Gulls squawk, sheep bray, waves gurgle. From the workshop a rhythmic clinking drifts on the breeze.

In the glass studio I find stunning pieces, sensual, resilient yet easily shattered. My fingers ache to make contact but signs all around say please do not handle. When I see the young man at the furnace a Renaissance description of glass comes to mind: *Delightful, Polite and Sightly*. I can't know whether he's *polite* or not! He gathers red liquid glass, blows a bubble, marvers it on stone. As he rotates the pontil rod, manipulates the malleable glass, I go into meltdown. He releases the piece with a swift sharp tap.

Now for my turn. In the heat of the moment my 'swift, sharp tap' has a ruinous affect; my masterpiece falls, hits the floor and shatters into fragments as I bolt the world of globs, frits and stringers, my face on fire.

I walk till the fire and the light fade. Down at the harbour the streets heave with eaters and drinkers dancing to a pop-Celtic band. Out to sea a Viking boat brightens, outlined in white lights; a silver moon hangs over the village. The vanishing sun reminds me, it's late in the day.

But perhaps it's not *too* late?

Cold, Cold Heart

Of late I'm fairly buoyant – until Marvin messages. Obsessed with all things arctic, he's progressed from padding around his apartment with a bag of Iceland peas on his head to stomping around a 'cryo-chamber', aka freezer, in boxers, crop-top, socks and clogs to music of his own choosing. For temperatures of minus 50C - the 'warm cabinet' - he'd gone, he says, for something lively. I'm wondering: *Abide with me?* I'm thinking back to our latest consult, when he'd shoved his latest offering at me; a damp, clammy, gruesome sheaf on the cryopreservation of a 'patient' he'd pilfered at some *Cryonics room party!!* He presents such morsels routinely, like a cat presenting a half-mangled trophy. But recalling that in place of vindictive triumph I'd seen only ghostly pallor, I feel a renewal of warmth for my last remaining patient before the ice encasing my mangled heart begins freezing over once more, plunging me back into darkness.

Dragon's Cave

The warmth that had drained from me leaving me shivering suffuses my body again as a London day dawns. The sky flares crimson, bathing my room in a rose-tinted light. All night, snatching myself from the brink of unconsciousness as though from a bottomless pit.

I dismiss the taxi a block from Farringdon. In Pret on Shoe Lane I eat porridge and gag; it could be the cement plopping round in the mixer outside.

At HQ I'm directed to a long, lonely table facing inquisitors seated in a horse-shoe arrangement. No good luck here. Step-father Philip, presiding, stands -the epitome of slick I notice, *except for his hands*. They're the thickset paws of a grizzly, mauling the papers, triggering a switch that throws light on a memory too dim to discern. All I catch as he hands down the 'sentence' are *review, standards* and *mandated by this board*.

The sky-lit ceiling clouds over; everything melts into shadow, giving the lie to a dawn that had augured so well and blighting my world.

Freudenschade

The world of science is celebrating art. Ed's friend Ted's play has opened to rapturous acclaim, somehow bringing me down. I escape into summer of 1912. Here's Jung in Zurich, eyes glinting bright like the sun in the lid of my coffee pot as he writes to Freud, proclaiming his trip to America.

Freud's reply is as cold as the grave: *'Dear Dr. Jung: I greet you, no longer affectionately, but still with satisfaction at your personal success'.*

He's referring to Jung's catch, the agoraphobic daughter of John D. Rockerfeller, Edith. She'd been in Zurich drawn by Jung's gravitational pull.

On her return to Chicago she isolates herself at her 1000 Lake Shore Drive mansion, afraid to venture out. Addicted to séances and reincarnation, convinced she's Tutankhamen's child-bride, the Princess Ankhesenemun, daughter of Pharaoh Akhenaten and Queen Nefertiti - she moves to a suite in the Drake Hotel overlooking Oak Street Beach where she dies, leaving barely a fistful of dollars.

In between worlds I pull myself together, warmly applauding Ted's achievement. But back in Vienna the world of Freud is *not* celebrating Jung. Freud grumbles to a fawning Ferenczi: *Jung landed himself a Rockefeller woman! I think with bitterness about the plight of our own Association'*

Face To Face

Wallowing in my own plight I go to my bookmarks and visit the website once more.

I'll be a good candidate as long as I have realistic expectations. The initial consult will be face to face with my surgeon who'll check for lopsidedness, facial palsy or *anything* that may be wrongly chalked up to the facelift.

I'm expecting to leave with a full head dressing and drain tubes, possibly pale, puffy, and feeling numb. Any swelling or bruising should only be temporary. I can manage pain with a strong analgesic but must refrain from *anything* that raises my pulse for at least three weeks!

Insurance doesn't cover elective procedures. Patients are largely satisfied and normally presentable within weeks to a month.

There is a very rare risk of scarring – (most patients don't notice until it's called to their attention) – or a loss of feeling in the lips.

Shortening of major muscles can occasionally cause dimples and skin slough.

Our plastic surgeons combine art with science. Entrust your face to us!

Godfather, Godman

Unhinged with mistrust and in two minds I retreat once more unto the breach where the European psyche is as splintered as mine. Godfather Freud and godman Jung symbolize the schism – the bourgeoisie versus bohemia, science versus spirit.

New Year

Jung has wished many more laurels to Freud's crown. But now, after leaving the Hauptbahnhof with Emma, just off the sixteen thirteen, he flails his arms and rails against Freud. Jung's had it with the 'coup d'état' - Freud now refers to *their* work as *his* movement – and of the weekly coffee, cake and squabbles of the Viennese, who seem to him rabble compared to Zurichers.

As the Jungs head for Bahnhofstrasse, passing through the triumphal arch, Freud in Vienna is at his wit's end. *Jung self-deified,* he splutters; *what next!* He's huffing around the *Zentralfriedhof,* Vienna's enormous cemetery, muttering. Could it be the popular saying *'half the size of Zurich but twice as much fun'?*

Here, by contrast, the whole world is finally one. Here are Russian, Romanian, Serbian and Coptic burial grounds; a Muslim site, Europe's first Buddhist cemetery, a plot for

Mormon deceased. There's a Catholic section, cemeteries for Lutherans, Calvinists and Evangelicals. Freud can't know that one of the Jewish cemeteries will be destroyed on *Kristallnacht,* or that later the Hebrew Centre for Brain Science will unite with Germans from the Max Planck Institute of Neurobiology, Freud's first field of study, to try to understand human behaviour and consciousness.

He should have such co-operation!

November

Jung returns from America a deviant from Freud's libido theory. Freud whines that his intention of 'amalgamating Jews and goyim in the service of psychoanalysis are separating like oil and water' - *no matter that he'd pressed Jewish colleagues to enlist Swiss Christians.* Stung, Jung moans that Freud has discredited him, suggesting that although he's no anti-Semite he might consider becoming one - *no matter that he fights to keep Jews in psychoanalytic practice and get the Führer certified mad.*

Here and There: Nineteen Twelve

Have I lapsed so far as to be certifiable? It seems this year, the year of my rebirth, we're living large in Europe. My man Akhenaten, the pharaoh who's handle on the *realpolitik* is off, is in therapy. Every shrink wants a piece of him.

One of Freud's protégés has analysed him, diagnosing an Oedipus Complex. *Is,* Akhenaten, they ponder - this mother-fixated neurotic who replaced his hated father with a father-god – the Oedipus of ancient Greek myth? Freud thinks not, though he does liken Pharaoh's paranoia to one Judge Schreber's in his virtual analysis based on Schreber's own memoir. Albeit one man's emission is another's celestial benediction, for Freud interprets the solar rays beating down on the judge as spermatazoon, Schreber as rays of god.

Which god held his breath that mankind came to its senses in Akhenaten's time? ponders Rilke, enthroned on his chateau's primitive privy, eavesdropping. Jung, only six months older than Rilke, doesn't deem him *quite* a contemporary, no matter that Rilke's biographer, translator at the Large Hadron Collider, will proclaim the poet's insight that all forces and consciousness are one aligns him with quantum theory.

Poet for poet, Akhenaten fares better. Jung is at one with the cult; his own magnum opus is rife with sun-worship as passionate as Pharaoh's. On cue, Pharaoh, who sees light as divine power, the source of all creation, offers up a poem to his new god, the sun-disc.

'When thou settest in the Western horizon, the earth is in darkness like the dead!'

Meanwhile, in the Western horizon I am lifted, sifted and dusted, my bindings of sand are feathered away, my head eased out like a baby. I'm here and there simultaneously; particle physics catches on in no time.

Love and War: Nineteen Twelve

- Inflaming Freud's dread of 'occultism' Jung refers to the libido as God, sun of 'the other world'.

- Nasa predicts a titanic collision between Andromeda and the Milky Way.

- As the unsinkable Titanic goes down the limestone head of Berlin's 'most beautiful Egyptian ambassador, Queen Nefertiti, rises.

- The Archbishop of Paris decrees Christians must not tango.

- At a congress in Munich arranged by Freud in the very Munich hotel where he and Wilhelm had their final, embittered meal, Jung, back from America, speaks to a psychoanalytic essay on Akhenaten who not only overthrew the existing culture *but even expunged his father's name.*

- Jung moans to Jones from the Viennese contingent that Freud thinks he, Jung, has a father complex against him and wishes him dead.

- Jones recalls noting that Freud, proposer of the Oedipus complex in which murderous undertones exist between father and son, is taking Jung's talk rather personally. Abruptly and without warning, Freud falls to the floor in a swooning faint.

- The sturdy Jung, now his arch-rival and enemy, lifts him tenderly into his arms and carries him to a couch.

'Some separations are inevitable and not a great loss', Freud says later. When asked about conflicts with colleagues. When asked about Jung he pauses and whispers, 'Jung was a very great loss'.

Marvin's Loss

Marve shrinks from my umbrella stand as though from a rearing horse. Apropos of nothing he tells me the rain that day had been *torrential,* a deluge of *mythic* proportions. I ask to what he refers. *'The flesh endures the roaring storms, the mind the past and futur*e, he says, misquoting Hobbs and handing me more stuff on Cryonics. I reluctantly learn that, when opting for cryo-preservation, at an extra cost having someone on standby when 'de-animation' occurs can help keep the brain's functionality.

Marve had taken this extra for *Mom!* - and had called when the moment was nigh. But Hans was in transit when de-animation occurred and could only send email instructions. *'Try swishing ice round the patient's head',* he advised.

Exporting Mom for Cryopreservation wasn't easy. Regulations on shipping of human remains insist death has complied with regional standards - by some definitions *the destruction of the human brain and the information within it.* Marve's mum was a gonner by any. After a terminal period of shock, dehydration, upregulation of coagulation factors and multiple organ failure, cryogenics was challenged before the team gained access. They went ahead anyway, with blood wash-out and antifreeze wash-in. The cryonaut's head was removed, packed in dry ice, stored in a giant Thermos at the temperature of liquid nitrogen and a cost of $40,000 for herself and $6,000 for the first fifteen pounds of her Alangu Mastiff, awaiting return to where friends are all dead and taxes outstanding.

Marve hands me a separate flyer: *Save your pets. When they're re-animated, extracting their information about you will be useful.* 'They reckoned if Mom stayed frozen for a few hundred years her brain could be thawed and fixed to a body cloned from her DNA. They said that would give time for compound interest on her money if it beat inflation by 3% per year'.

'I just didn't get it', he says. 'She hated my stupidity; I always made her lose face'.

Losing Face: Dry Run

'It's useful to do a practice run the day before a SMAS facelift surgery. Incision points can be marked out, a bit like a map of the celestial bodies. Mark the position of the Zygomaticus major muscle as a radiating pattern with Methylene blue tattoos or a red, extra-fine Sharpie marker'.

'With the face upright, grasp sections of skin and pull them upwards. Mentally note how far you can stretch it and the strength of pulling that gives optimal contours. It's like pitching a tent; each peg you put in will tighten the fabric. Plot and mark strategic 'pegs' carefully spaced, and others in between for an even tension. Avoid a level of tension that will distort facial features.

Tunnelling To The Beginning Of Time*: 5

Tensions are high at the Large Hadron Collider when operations are suddenly halted. At the precise moment an explosion contaminates the vacuum pipe, I'm lying half-in half-out of consciousness in an out-of-body experience looking down on my body.

I watch Philip's abettor Denis arrive in theatre. Yanking at the overhead light and looking down on my face, he complains that the Methylene blue tattoos have faded and replaces them with crosses using a number fifteen blade.

Working through incisions he talks to himself distractedly. '*Was* that the Orbicularis?' He unsteadily curves the incision forward, grasps the SMAS pulling it this way and that like a kite flyer adjusting his course, yanks it up with Allis clamps and fixes it, complaining of feeling exhausted.

Next the Zygomaticus, the strongest muscle of oral expression. He grasps the belly with forceps and gives it a good tug upwards. 'Why then are the Modiolus Labii not observed to be lifting', he ponders, muttering 'if all connections to the skin aren't freed she'll be as dimpled as a baby's bum'. With a tremor he severs the Zig ligaments, reconstructs them with sutures, lifts the Modiolar and fixes it to the stump. He anchors the flap, sutures with five-point Prolene and P1 needles, trims dog ears from the hairline and closes with staples.

Steri-Strips are placed on the wounds. I leave the theatre with a white knitted pressure-dressing bound round my head like something from the Curse of the Mummy's Tomb after Denis has checked for dimpling, guessing out loud that it is probably moderate. Wondering whether it would look like natural dimples if permanent depressions existed he makes the judgment that it would.

*One-time mission statement of The Large Hadron Collider**

In Damnatio Memorae

Akhenaten thinks *his* judgement is sound but now, worrying at the tie that holds his false beard, he acknowledges disaster is imminent.

He's diverted from a parasitic court and priesthood opulence, luxury, ornate perfumed mansions and country estates to create an egalitarian society, enraging the beneficiaries of the traditional chief God Amun-Re. He's upped-sticks them from Thebes and banished the pantheon entire. Gone are Hathor, Cow-Headed Goddess of Love, Motherhood and Drunkenness; redundant the Protector of Deceased Peoples' Stomachs. *Aten* the sun-disc, whose light shines impartially, alone prevails.

Nefertiti also knows their number is up; her premonition came the day of the banquet.
Amidst dancing, clapping, leaps and handstands, backbends, splits and twirls without end, *she'd* felt the cold hand of doom.

The first mortal blow is a crushing revenge; one of their daughters dies. Their indescribable grief weeps down the ages in dark, bat-infested tombs.

Soon most of the household are gone; two daughters alone remain. Successors delete all trace of the family. Sarcophagi are smashed, mummies torn to shreds, as though they had never existed. The winds of the desert blow for aeons; temples, palaces and dynasties are buried in their wake, the limestone head of Nefertiti is interred in rubble and sand. The beautiful face is no more.

Or is it?

PART FIVE
COALESCENCE

Saving Face

I burn up just *envisaging* the op. An early night and a wedge of Gruyere bring indigestion and nightmares. Giles appears first; *Let me pay for repairs to your face!* he says. I refuse the offer without animosity. Next up, Nefertiti's head looking down on her mummification. Her abdomen is open, all organs except for her heart, thought to be the centre of being and intelligence, removed. She's dried out with salt, filled with Myrrh and Cassia and swathed in strips of linen a thousand yards in length without a joint Her brain, thought to be useless, is hooked out through her nose and discarded.

As my alter is dispatched to the Osirian underworld awaiting a fun-filled eternity, I'm lying prepped and anaesthetised with a line of Kefzol in my arm.

The procedure is hailed successful, the anaesthetic uneventful. I'm through to ICU when impaired thermo-regulatory control makes my temperature plummet to the levels of a hibernating squirrel. My extremities are like ice as blood is shunted to my core, protecting vital organs. Muscles in my hands and feet fatigue, relax, open up; blood rushes to them. I feel over-heated even as my temperature is dropping. Rousing from anaesthesia while in a state of hypothermia I tear at my back-fastening gown in a frenzy of what medics call Paradoxical Undressing and mountaineers Cold Stupid.

The Spectacular Mechanical Chronometer

I'm cool and upbeat when Marvin arrives bearing gifts; he'd been seduced by a pre-launch campaign.

'Due out soon, its pulsing energy is already tangible in the horological world'.

It's a spectacular mechanical chronometer with a Mother-of Pearl dial, two baguette sapphires and six round diamonds. It's not lost on me that it's Mother's Day and as soon as I'm out of the clinic I auction the watch on eBay to fund transference of fat from the adipose depot on my butt to my face.

It's a breeze compared to the remedial op; the mere three suture lines are neat as needlepoint by Oblate Sisters of Jesus the Priest.

I'm not sure about the result though. My new face though beautiful is mask-like.

Divine Union

Cornwall

Masking indifference and numb with cold I follow a diminutive flock into the old stone church near the cottage. Inside, in the gloom, my senses are time machines taking my mind to new levels: textured hassocks as coarse as harsh bark; walls and pillars, imbued with invocations, alive to my touch as flesh; the musty smell, *the 'feeling'* once spoiled by lack-love, lack-lustre vicars obscure as the Akond of Swat: their spouting eyebrows antennae, picking up sin; their funereal voices deep as the grave; in their billowing cassocks at the back of the church taking puffs from a Players Navy Cut.

But now heady memories surface; of glittering moon-lit lanes leading to candlelight mass, the nativity glistening on pitch-black nights. My closet love rises. I surrender to the stillness, vaguely recalling some warning against spiritual ecstasy and psycho-physical trances. I don't care. As I reach for my altered state I shift through spacetime to a parallel image:

Greece:

Slithering down slopes of searing sand to the voluptuous

shade of a thermal bath, a cathedral of sorts, surrounded by riotous, headily fragrant *Jasminum Officinale* - known as *Poet's Jasmine* for its euphoric, aphrodisiac properties. The thick-walled spa's high vaulted ceiling; small openings to the sky bright as stars; beneath hot water spouting from gargoyles, a smooth stone floor, sensual beyond words to the feet.

That stone-walled spa aroused 'the feeling', jolting me back to my exhibition and a terrifying ex-pat matriarch spitting out words from my artist statement: *'These works pay homage to the sensual and spiritual which the artist regards as one'.*

As dormant forces flare into life I'm lifted by the rainbow-tinted light; soaring vaulting raises me up. From towering peaks and fiery sunsets, from the stained-glass masterpiece of Saint Chappelle to the celestial dome of the Lotfollah Mosque to sensuous carvings of Buddha, emblems of other worldliness, channelled through the senses, suffuse me with light and warmth, banishing shadows.

Dragon Slain

Indistinct as a face coming out of the shadows, memories, gradually discernible.

Before:

- Philip, grappling with his cup like a man with a club hand trying to pluck a harp, turns up the dimmer on a past as elusive as dreams.
- The drawbridge defending the bastion slams down; memories gush out, threatening to shatter my fortress.

Bile rises like magma. I invoke an ebullient Warrior, set a bully to catch a bully, spill the beans to Philip's father about:

- Visiting Philip's mother; wetting myself as we left.
- Philip yanking at the blinds in her room, unveiling like some masterpiece borders of withered perennials bowing their heads as though weeping, yelling '_Say hello to May!_'
- Grace's nurse Ruth holding her hand, reading out her notes: _Dysphagia. Hemiplegia, expressive Aphasia - the loss of ability to speak the words you're thinking._
- Philip feeding Grace at dinner, pretending the spoon was a nose-diving plane, scraping her lips after each as though grouting till Grace noticed Ruth in the car

park, leaving and taking her things.

- Grace flailing her good arm to catch Ruth's attention, wailing and beating her face. Philip whipping off Grace's collar, bellowing for help. There was only a cleaner available.

- Philip yelling at the cleaner 'sort out Slobberchops!' The cleaner placing her walking frame out of her reach, Philip pinning Grace to the chair.

- After twenty-five minutes her wailing dropping to a whimper; Grace struggling to catch Philip's eye as though trying to lift her head was like trying to hoist a drawbridge with an army stampeding over it.

After:

- A cleansing, a freeing up of psychic space in a memory dump of all time. _It was nothing I did!_

- Thanks to Qi Gong, Zazen, Yoga, Tapping or Omega 3 - or none of the above - hitting Pay Dirt; finding myself undivided.

- Compassion flooding my being; for Marvin, for _my_ inner Marvin, for everyone up to and including the clinic. (Doesn't stop me suing their glutes though.)

- My virtual companions fading into history; Philip ebbing away like a spring low tide at new moon.

- Coming through my review with dazzling lucidity.

Moonlight Catharsis

By moonlight, a dash to the all-night pharmacy for Gaviscon then prostrate on the sofa watching Film 4. *Your dismissal of me as numbing as Novocaine.* I go out fearlessly, get bludgeoned, dismantled, and have to start over all over. What blossomed like a gorgeous firework fizzled out like a dud.
The soul does not weary but aches.

Without warning, something powerful and tender throbbing in my lips, like sensual living creatures palpitating. The life force courses through me, an intense sensuality. We groaned like lost people, fell on each other like savages. Our earthy carnality ignited fierce life that lives on. In daring to follow our hearts 'it is to self we come'*.

Migration of Souls

London: New Year's Eve
The night sky's on fire with The Eye's pyrotechnic eruptions. Phosphorescent pods shower Technicolor gems on Big Ben as Alison piles on the ordure. Giles feels his eyes swivel like Catherine Wheels when she dumps him. Out with the old, in with the new.

America
Alison, returned to her roots, hits the I-94 to Chicago where her gallery's floors shine like mirrors for the private view for a man called Vadim.

London
Giles has a Romanian lodger. As he lays down the rules, Nicolae retreats. Giles feels remorse as he pierces Nic's back with a stare then goes back to his tunes - vintage Sixties.

Romania; The Sixties
When Vadim leaves Romania there's Flower-Power in California, free love of a different kind at home. Ceausescu, 'Genius of the Carpathians', 'The Danube of Thought', wants the population doubled. Erection-led Vadim can help. Known as Vad the Impaler, he numbers Nicolae among his progeny. He escapes to the States.

London

Nicolae's remembering State 'care' - running naked, freezing and hungry; it was Vadim's mother who'd sprung him. He rustles up supper in the crepe pan and burns it. Giles won't mind, they'll pick one up in Ikea.

Between worlds.

After the opening Vadim flies to London. He prods at the Foie-Gras in Filo - it's all pie in the sky to him. He adjusts the plastic fan that demarks his territory in business class.

London

Giles is alright; it's Nicolae with whom he's now joined; not in holy acrimony at St Andrew-by-the-Wardrobe, but in Civil Partnership at Walthamstow Registry Office. He's swapping Grandad's pad for a dilapidated chateau in Slovakia. It's a wreck but they love it.

The Uluburun Wreck
(and Talatat Tales)

A few years after Nefertit's demanifestation, around 1316 BCE, a ship sets sail on the quantum ocean. It's carrying a protecting divinity but the gods aren't appeased. A tidal wave sends her plunging to the deeps past astonished cephalopods with gaping mouths to be shrouded in bindings of seaweed and buried in a watery tomb.

Until that is, the frequency formerly known as twentieth century A.D. when quantum physicists suggest linear time may not exist and parallel universes probably do; that the cosmos exists complete as infinite, shimmering possibilities.

One shimmering day a diver off Turkey surfaces, not with sponges, but with debris from a Late Bronze age ship dendrochronologists date around 1316 BCE. There are elephant tusk trumpets, tortoiseshell lutes, olives, almonds, coriander, figs, and among eighteen thousand artefacts, a gold scarab seal with the name of Queen Nefertiti.

****

In the same frequency an incompetent hack, finding 'his scoop' already on some website, hacks out the hard drive, gobs on it, stamps on it and drives it like a fury to the tip, thinking that in destroying hardware he'll wipe virtual content.

Alchemising magic with physics, Eric, a geek working shifts to fund upgrades, reclaims the hard drive revealing obsessive visits in the browsing history to a site showing numerous images of Nefertiti and Akhenaten's family engraved on thirty-five thousand *Talatat* blocks resurrected from smashed, defaced, jumbled rubble filling the pillars of their successor's temple and impossible to reconstruct until the advent of computers and people like Eric.

Nefertiti's departure may be shrouded in mystery, but her name lives on. And who knows whether, with an infallible instinct for survival, she reincarnates, rises meteorically up the ladder of a corporate giant, invests in shares which strong commodity prices and high-profile takeovers push up the Footsie, and as back up, marries a Seventh Day Adventist roll-over jackpot winner for love *as well as* for money.

Barackhenaten

Akhenaten the maverick pharaoh, also resurrected, is the spiritual ancestor of prophets according to a Rosicrucian order dedicated to him, in which he's proclaimed a projection in Plane Earth of the goddess of harmony, justice, and truth.

Views vary. In Plane Earth he's also 'the crackpot Crackhenaten' according to the British Museum's keeper of Egyptian antiquities, or 'the wrecker' of idiosyncratic 'Omm Sety' aka Dorothy Eady, who berated excavators at the Akhenaten Temple Project for 'working on that S.O.B'.

More favourably, he's Breasted's 'first individual', Petrie's genius who crushed superstition, Freud's founder of Abrahamic religions, Jung's visionary who united god archetypes, Rilke's game changer and Glass's inspired firebrand in his haunting opera '*Akhnaten*' - the third of a trilogy bundling him with Einstein and Ghandi as transformers of their times. For certain, Pearson's androgynous 'Magician' and Meade's Mythical King is a King with the Elvis factor who inspires Khalo, Freud, Jarman and Glass to produce paintings, books, films and operas about him.

There are *also* those who think President Obama is a double of Pharaoh Akhenaten and Michelle a dead ringer for his mother. Prophesy seekers ponder whether the First Family are clones, based on the news that human genetic material extracted from an Egyptian mummy contains DNA that *could be* cloned in a plasmid vector.

He and his lady planned for life eternal and, with better outcomes than many an insurance plan, have it, in *Ameti,* sky home of the immortals.

Reunion

The sky is a luminous, ominous grey; heavy with gathering conflict.

Jung's never seen it snow so slowly. Bumper flakes thicken the air to a fleck-speckled fog, shrouding Lake Zurich, changing his world.

Turbulent dreams and torrents of emotion beset him; his world is a-tremble. His psyche, container of his consciousness, is troubled and the world, he believes, only exists when consciously reflected. He, a man whose psychology synthesises body and soul, who knows beyond doubt the interconnectedness of all things, feels split. He reads Sigmund's letter again.

'Dear doctor Jung; I propose we abandon our personal relations entirely'.

How did their impassioned friendship end in a split as improbable as splitting the atom? Jung, a man with knowledge of Eastern and Western philosophy, myth, alchemy and comparative religions, gazes down from the turret of his house like the Lady of Shallot, knowing *not* what the curse may be.

Hypnotic snowflakes continue veiling the Lake.

He goes to his study, submits himself to his unconscious, excavating building blocks he loved as a child from the prehistoric cavern of his mind. On resurfacing he devotedly creates, tongue between his lips, cottages, castles and villages, elevating play to a ritual, ecstatic to know he's releasing blocked energy. Prolific works follow.

Destruction as a Necessity for Becoming*

Jung believes contact between two personalities is like that between chemical substances; that if there's any reaction, both are transformed.

Aeons ago Earth was one supercontinent *Pangea* till it split and land masses drifted apart. Time passed. Two land masses moved closer until they collided. Pushing against each other they caused the seabed to buckle and rear up, creating the mighty Himalayas.

In the beginning, a voice from the unknown multitude answers Freud's; that voice is Jung's, whose veneration for Freud is like a 'religious crush'. In the end, seething divisions foreshadow disaster like fissures across the earth's crust as Tectonic plates shift with a force that will blow them apart.

Snapping and snarling. Freud's position is 'at heel'. *'You, while behaving abnormally insists he's normal'!* he berates Jung.

Jung, a muscle-rippling puppy, squirming, leaping, excited beyond endurance, sinking his teeth in, sees through *Freud's* little tricks…

Jung is guided by 'the inner realm of light'; Freud, man of hard science, thinks that's all mystical woo. But both are wounded by the split; both suffer the agonies of rebirth before re-emerging as eternal figures of the magnitude of each other's dreams.

Perhaps they're two sides of one coin; two mega-stars trying to share the same firmament. Though hampered by their personalities they no doubt suspected 'the other' to be *their own* otherness - all they were at one with and all that they were not.

* *Title of the thesis of Sabina Speilrein, protégé of Freud and rumoured lover of Jung.*

Umbraphobia

London

Marve's not at one. He's on a mission, determined, battling against the sun in his eyes somewhere between Tottenham Court Road and the British Museum when panic consumes him; he senses a presence behind him. Swivelling around to face his assailant he's confronted by his own shadow.

He's a wreck on merely _approaching_ the store. Large letters high on the grey stone façade - a siren song, luring him to his nemesis and doom - proclaim unequivocally:

UMBRELLAS!

Like sentinels guarding the vestibule to destiny, vertical glass panels trumpet the name of James Smith & Sons. The letters swim towards him as he walks through the door and into the past.

For many, this emporium is a paradise of walking sticks, seat sticks, doorman's and regular use umbrellas, animal head handle umbrellas with the rams and stag horn crooks, charming parasols and gleaming canes.

To him it's the mouth of the dragon's cave.

Curved glass cabinets with carved rearing animals watchful as gargoyles turn to a whirling centrifuge inside which he is splayed and spinning, plastered to its wall.

On coming back to consciousness he's escorted to a chair. To overcome nausea he turns his mind to facts instilled in immersion therapy. Fact: for ancient Egyptians umbrellas symbolised the vault over heaven, for ancient Greeks an erotic motif in the Bacchanal; Indian kings were Brothers of the Sun and the Moon, Lords of the Umbrella.

He sways as he pays for a most elegant lady's umbrella, (mock-crystal mallard-head handle), and leaves. But slumped crumpled and moist in a cab to Heathrow, he's *triumphant.* He's *'the most excellent Majesty of Thunaparanta, Tampadipa and all umbrella-wearing chiefs of the East' – a glorious footprint in the sands of time.

*Tavernier's 'Voyage to the East' (C17)

Awakening

<u>Egypt</u>
Sands lash the Valley for aeons, sealing entrances to underground chambers where deified humanity lies mummified in sarcophagi of gold between visible and invisible worlds.

The sands give up secrets.

The limestone head of Nefertiti, resting in timespans for millennia, in parallel worlds on a plane of suspended animation, is awakened by her prince, a German excavator, three thousand, two hundred and fifty-nine years after she was said to be laid there.

Could it be that her black outlined eyes open wide with surprise, one eye falls out, rolls over the sand and into oblivion?

For certain she's conceded to the Germans; the Egyptians attempt to barter, Hitler later requisitions her and buries her once more in a salt mine, from whence she's recovered by American troops who donate her to the Egyptian Museum in Berlin, her final resting place.

Has there been chicanery in the desert? Did a fake or replica slip through the sands of time?

No matter. Nefertiti is risen. She walks with mortals as the face gazing out from carrier bags at Cairo International duty-free shop.

As an elixir for eternal youth, early death sucks. But Nefertiti, like Elvis and Marylin, finds it. And she's departed from me but I've kept my own counsel, adopted the alias Nefertiti Beatty and moved to Lucerne.

Forever and Ever

Cameras capture Marvin hurrying across the Kapellbrücke, struggling down the Haldenstrasse and up the funicular with aforementioned umbrella and another gift plucked from the ether via eBay. He crosses the lobby of the landmark hotel and mounts the spiral staircase to my new, swish Swiss apartment, lunging at sweat as it falls from his brow, rubbing his face like Macbeth trying to wipe away blood. Down in the restaurant with views of the mountains and lake he re-gifts me *the spectacular mechanical chronometer!* As I slip it on, its diamonds throw off lights like a glitter-ball. *I'm* in my element; behind my back in classical reliefs reminiscent of temple décor, Cleopatra tumbles from a rug and greets Caesar with the loose-limbed writhing and ecstatic arched lifts of Egyptian court dancers.

'Material', I whisper, turning to Marve, 'has escaped through the tunnels of consciousness to the chambers of your unconscious mind. But irrepressible Eros the life-force will not remain buried forever!'

Today I'm glowing from the fiery late sun and my out of court settlement. Behind my back on a kid-soft couch a recumbent Marve rabbits on. I want to say sorry your time's

up, but if it doesn't exist how can I?
When the loss adjustor calls I'm smiling inscrutably, feeling
almost translucent, macraméing beard-ties for Pharaoh.

Amen

JACQUELINE SULLIVAN is an artist, writer and lecturer in art and creative writing prior to which she was a postgraduate student at Goldsmiths and University of the Arts, London UK and Head of Arts in continuing education.

Her other fiction has appeared in winner's anthologies and literary journals, including several of those in this volume, and her articles and reviews in literary and fine art journals. Her art has been exhibited in London and Europe and is in private collections there and the USA, Brazil and Canada.

In No Time, her first full-length work, builds on a theme explored in a series of paintings from her exhibition 'Delfos', which can be viewed with a selection of her other art and stories at her website shown below.

More about Jacqueline at jacquelinesullivanartwords.com

Printed in Great Britain
by Amazon